This book is dedicated to
Mummy's dogson Odd Mathias
who loves aeroplanes;
Mummy's dogdaughter
and friend of Rolly Trolly, Maya;
and to my dogfriend Kasper
who loves me!

Love Finse

THIS BOOK
BELONGS TO

_____

_____

"Finse Explores Scandinavia"

The right of Karine Hagen to be identified as the author
and Suzy-Jane Tanner to be identified as the illustrator
of this work has been asserted by them in accordance
with the Copyright Designs and Patents Act 1988.

Text copyright © Karine Hagen 2015
Illustrations copyright © Suzy-Jane Tanner 2015

First published by Viking Cruises 2015. Reprinted 2016
83 Wimbledon Park Side, London, SW19 5LP

ISBN 978-1-909968-08-0

www.finse.me

Produced by Colophon Digital Projects Ltd,
Old Isleworth, TW7 6RJ, United Kingdom
Printed in China.

FINSE EXPLORES SCANDINAVIA

Karine Hagen
Suzy-Jane Tanner

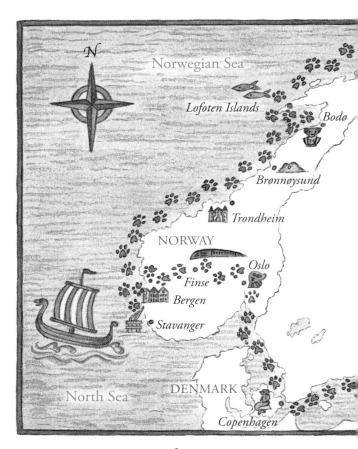

N

Norwegian Sea

Lofoten Islands

Bodø

Brønnøysund

Trondheim

NORWAY

Oslo

Finse

Bergen

Stavanger

North Sea

DENMARK

Copenhagen

Tromsø

SWEDEN

Rovaniemi

FINLAND

FINSE
EXPLORES
SCANDINAVIA

Stockholm

Baltic Sea

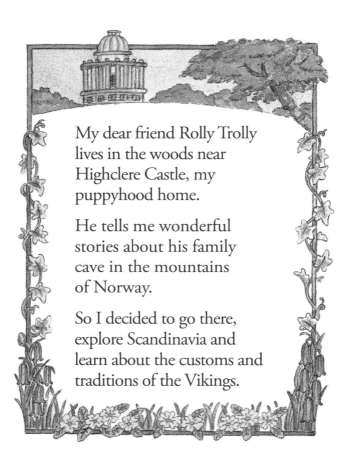

My dear friend Rolly Trolly lives in the woods near Highclere Castle, my puppyhood home.

He tells me wonderful stories about his family cave in the mountains of Norway.

So I decided to go there, explore Scandinavia and learn about the customs and traditions of the Vikings.

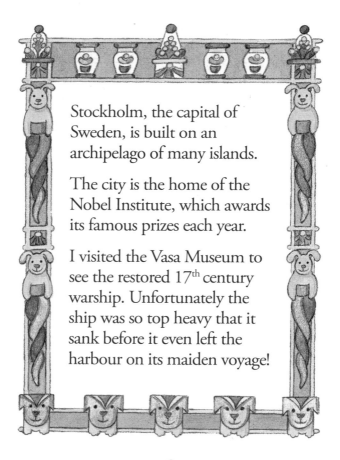

Stockholm, the capital of Sweden, is built on an archipelago of many islands.

The city is the home of the Nobel Institute, which awards its famous prizes each year.

I visited the Vasa Museum to see the restored 17th century warship. Unfortunately the ship was so top heavy that it sank before it even left the harbour on its maiden voyage!

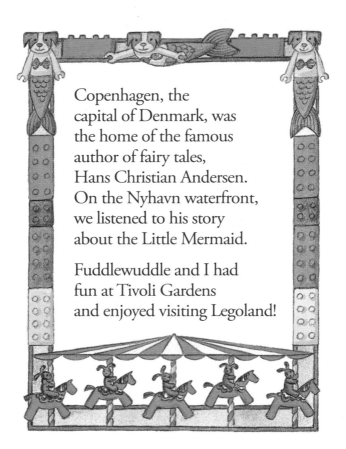

Copenhagen, the
capital of Denmark, was
the home of the famous
author of fairy tales,
Hans Christian Andersen.
On the Nyhavn waterfront,
we listened to his story
about the Little Mermaid.

Fuddlewuddle and I had
fun at Tivoli Gardens
and enjoyed visiting Legoland!

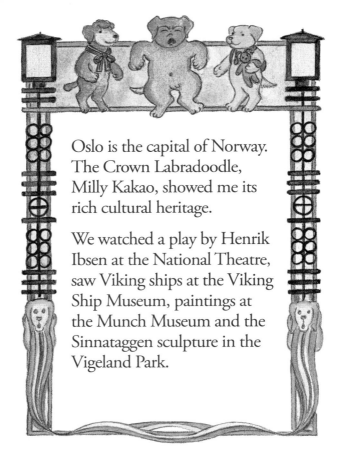

Oslo is the capital of Norway. The Crown Labradoodle, Milly Kakao, showed me its rich cultural heritage.

We watched a play by Henrik Ibsen at the National Theatre, saw Viking ships at the Viking Ship Museum, paintings at the Munch Museum and the Sinnataggen sculpture in the Vigeland Park.

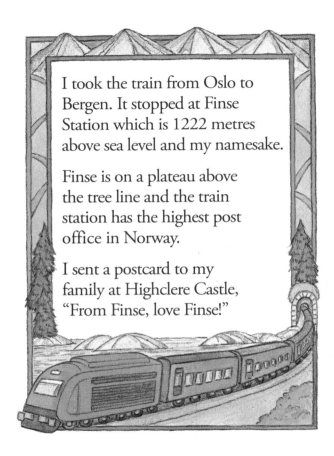

I took the train from Oslo to Bergen. It stopped at Finse Station which is 1222 metres above sea level and my namesake.

Finse is on a plateau above the tree line and the train station has the highest post office in Norway.

I sent a postcard to my family at Highclere Castle, "From Finse, love Finse!"

Finse
1222m

13

Bergen was founded in 1070 on a Viking site.

For nearly 500 years the city was the trading centre for the Hanseatic League of German merchants.

The composer Edvard Grieg was born in Bergen. I visited his house, Troldhaugen, now a museum, and saw the hut where he composed music.

Stavanger is the centre of the Norwegian oil industry.

Tradition has it that the Viking, Erik the Red, sailed from near here.

His son, Leif Eriksson, was an explorer and is my great hero. He reached America 500 years before Christopher Columbus. He landed in Labrador where my ancestors came from.

Nidaros Cathedral in
Trondheim is the largest
medieval building in Norway.

The city is the country's capital
of technology and home of
the world famous Norwegian
Institute of Technology. My
human grandfather Tor, who is
very intelligent, studied there.

I visited Rolly Trolly's family in the Torghatten mountain near Brønnøysund.

They looked rather scary but, unlike most trolls, they were very friendly and welcomed me to their home in a deep cave and told me tales from Norse mythology.

17th May is Norway's National Day. Fuddlewuddle and I each wore a *bunad*, the traditional costume. There is a different design for each region of the country.

Everyone looks forward to the *sankthansaften* celebrations on the night of 23rd June when there are parties and bonfires.

The beautiful Lofoten
Islands are off the coast of
Bodø. There are six large
and many smaller islands.

Stockfish are cod that are
caught here. They are dried
on wooden racks and then
exported all over the world.
They are a key ingredient
of Bacalao, the famous
fish stew.

Tromsø is 300 km inside the Arctic Circle. In summer, the sun hardly sets, and you can even see it at midnight. I picked delicious cloudberries. *Nam nam!*

In the winter the sun hardly rises. Then there is a good chance that you will see the wonderful Aurora Borealis or Northern Lights.

I visited Lapland, home
of the Sami people, which
covers parts of Norway,
Sweden, Finland and Russia.

It is the home of the
Santa Claus Village.

Santa and his elves
gave me a model of a
Viking longboat for
Rolly Trolly, to remind
him of his home.

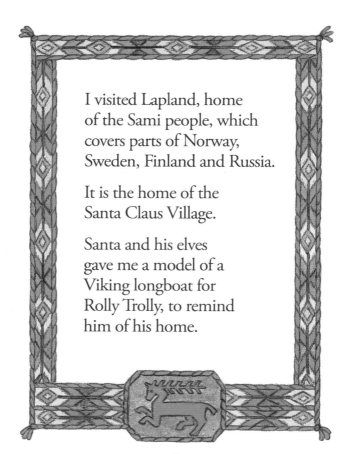

It was time to say goodbye,
but in true Viking spirit
I will continue exploring
the world.

Goodbye Scandinavia!
Adjø Skandinavia!
Farvel Skandinavien!
Hyvästi Skandinavia!

DOGOLOGY

I was honoured to meet the Crown Labradoodle of Norway, many other fine Scandinavian dogs, and even some very friendly trolls!